FIVE LIES THAT RUIN
RELATIONSHIPS

FIVE LIES THAT RUIN RELATIONSHIPS: WRONG BELIEFS PRODUCE WRONG BEHAVIORS

FIVE LIES THAT RUIN
RELATIONSHIPS

TABLE OF CONTENTS

FIVE LIES THAT RUIN
RELATIONSHIPS

CHIP INGRAM

Dear Friends,

Welcome to *Five Lies that Ruin Relationships: Wrong Beliefs Produce Wrong Behaviors.*

God longs for us to have right relationships with Him and our spouse, family and friends! He longs for intimacy, peace, love and joy to reign in our hearts for our hearts are the wellspring of life. So, what is getting in the way of experiencing that kind of intimacy in your relationships?

In the next 10 weeks, we will unpack five lies that have the potential to ruin relationships with those we love. We'll also examine the source of quarreling, how our words can wound others, how not to make decisions, and why better things don't always make things better.

I encourage you to take some time and get to know the people in your group. Remember, that real life change happens in the context of community. Sharing openly, honestly, and authentically when appropriate with your group will create an environment where God has access to your heart. He longs to do a great work in you so that He can do great works through you!

My prayer for you and your group is for restoration in all your relationships as modeled by the redeeming love of our Savior.

Keep pressin' ahead,

Chip Ingram
President and Teaching Pastor,
Living on the Edge

SESSION 1:
WHY WE FIGHT WITH THOSE WE LOVE

VIDEO NOTES:

> ## LIE 1: "SENSUAL PLEASURE WILL SATISFY MY INNER LONGINGS FOR HAPPINESS."

What is the source of quarrels and conflicts among you? Is not the source your pleasures that wage war in your members? You lust and do not have; so you commit murder. You are envious and cannot obtain; so you fight and quarrel. You do not have because you do not ask. You ask and do not receive, because you ask with wrong motives, so that you may spend it on your pleasures. **JAMES 4: 1-3** (NASB)

THE CAUSE: The root cause of interpersonal conflicts is our consuming passion for

_____.

-|- **OUR PROBLEM =**

-|- **THE SYMPTOMS =**

-|- **OUR STRATEGY =**

-|- **THE RESULTS =**

GOD'S DIAGNOSIS: Our constant quarrels reveal . . .

You adulteresses, do you not know that friendship with the world is hostility toward God? Therefore whoever wishes to be a friend of the world makes himself an enemy of God. Or do you think that the Scripture speaks to no purpose: "He jealously desires the Spirit which He has made to dwell in us"? But He gives a greater grace Therefore it says, "GOD IS OPPOSED TO THE PROUD, BUT GIVES GRACE TO THE HUMBLE." **JAMES 4: 4-6** (NASB)

-|- **WE'VE BELIEVED A LIE.**

-|- **WE'VE BETRAYED A TRUST.**

-|- **WE'VE BECOME AN ENEMY.**

DISCUSSION QUESTIONS:

1. Have the courage to answer the first question Chip asked. On a scale of 1 to 10, with 1 being a "perfect saint" and 10 being a "spiritual adulterer," where is your Christian walk in relation to the world? Why?

2. How did the first story Chip told about the divorce strike you? What did you feel? Did it remind you of a conflict you have gone through?

3. What is at the core of all our conflict?

4. Depending on how comfortable you are in the group, explain how your own selfishness has led to conflict in your own life.

5. What are some ways you have fallen in the trap of believing the world's system?

SESSION 1: KEYS

CONFLICT WITH LOVED ONES IS AN INEVITABLE PART OF LIFE

THE SOURCE OF OUR CONFLICT RESIDES IN OUR OWN SELFISH-NESS

"It would seem that Our Lord finds our desires not too strong, but too weak. We are half-hearted creatures, fooling about with drink and sex and ambition when infinite joy is offered us, like an ignorant child who wants to go on making mud pies in a slum because he cannot imagine what is meant by the offer of a holiday at the sea. We are far too easily pleased."

C.S. LEWIS

ACTION STEPS:

Time for personal reflection and determined action.

Are there any unresolved conflicts in your life right now?

As easy as it would be to write down how those conflicts have hurt you, what part has your desire for self-gratification created problems in your relationships?

Write their names down and begin to pray that God will give you the courage and the tools to reconcile those relationships. Chances are it won't be easy and next week we will learn about God's prescription for healing.

AT HOME:

None of us like to hear that we may be an "enemy of God." However, when bitterness and anger seep into our horizontal relationships, it affects our vertical relationship with our Father in heaven. Chip mentioned that when we live worldly, God puts us in a "velvet vice." God squeezes our hearts to produce character. Take a few moments to read Hebrews 12:4-11.

As you meditate on these verses, write down some thoughts to these questions:

-|- What does God's discipline prove about our relationship with Him?

-|- What does God's discipline produce in our life?

-|- How have you experienced God's discipline in your life?

MEMORY VERSES: JAMES 4:1-3 (NASB)

What is the source of quarrels and conflicts among you? Is not the source your pleasures that wage war in your members? You lust and do not have; so you commit murder. You are envious and cannot obtain; so you fight and quarrel. You do not have because you do not ask. You ask and do not receive, because you ask with wrong motives, so that you may spend it on your pleasures.

DEFUSING CONFLICT...
RESTORING
RELATIONSHIPS

VIDEO NOTES:

GOD'S DIAGNOSIS: Our constant quarrels reveal...

1. We've believed a lie.

2. We've betrayed a trust.

3. We've become an enemy.

You adulteresses, do you not know that friendship with the world is hostility toward God? Therefore whoever wishes to be a friend of the world makes himself an enemy of God. Or do you think that the Scripture speaks to no purpose: "He jealously desires the Spirit which He has made to dwell in us?" But He gives a greater grace Therefore it says, "GOD IS OPPOSED TO THE PROUD, BUT GIVES GRACE TO THE HUMBLE." **JAMES 4: 4-6** (NASB)

GOD'S PRESCRIPTION: _____
and God will heal your relationships. v7-10

Submit therefore to God. Resist the devil and he will flee from you. Draw near to God and He will draw near to you. Cleanse your hands, you sinners; and purify your hearts, you double-minded. Be miserable and mourn and weep; let your laughter be turned into mourning and your joy to gloom. Humble yourselves in the presence of the Lord, and He will exalt you.
JAMES 4: 7-10 (NASB)

STEPS TO DEFUSE CONFLICT

1. _____

"Submit yourselves therefore to God . . ." **v7a**

2. _____

"Resist the devil and he will flee from you." **v7b**

3. _____

"Draw near to God and He will draw near to you." **v8**

4. _____

"Cleanse your hands . . . purify your hearts . . ." **v8b**
"Let there be tears for the wrong you've done . . ." **v9**

GOD'S PROMISE FOR THE HUMBLE v10

DISCUSSION QUESTIONS:

1. What was the new insight you received that will help bring you genuine reconciliation of relationships?

2. How did Chip define "hedonism"?

3. Why is hedonism a lie? How are we influenced unconsciously to "buy into" its philosophy daily?

4. Chip talked about the need for a "you all" group. What have been the best places for you to connect with a group of people to challenge and encourage you?

5. If you feel comfortable, tell a story about how you genuinely repented and humbled yourself before someone else and it helped reconcile a relationship.

SESSION 2: KEYS

OUR HEDONISM STEMS FROM A DESIRE FOR POSSESSIONS, PLEASURE, OR POWER

REPENTANCE MEANS A CHANGE OF MIND THAT LEADS TO A CHANGE OF ACTION

"The old Puritans used to pray for 'the gift of tears.' If ever you cease to know the virtue of repentance, you are in darkness. Examine yourself and see if you have forgotten how to be sorry."[1]

OSWALD CHAMBERS

[1] Oswald Chambers, *My Utmost for His Highest : Selections for the Year* (Grand Rapids, MI: Discovery House Publishers, 1993, c1935), December 7.

ACTION STEPS:

We easily blame others, the world, or Satan for falling into temptation. However, listen to James as he reveals the real source of our temptation, "But each person is tempted when he is lured and enticed by his *own* desire" (1:14, emphasis mine). Chip mentioned three areas where we fall. By each one, write down how you struggle with each and what you are doing to fight Satan in those areas (i.e. go on a media fast):

-I- A desire to have (possessions)

-I- A desire to feel (pleasure)

-I- A desire to be (power)

AT HOME:

Defusing conflict sounds like defusing a bomb – unless you proceed carefully, someone is liable to get hurt. What are the hidden agendas you haven't surrendered to God? Are you fighting against Satan or letting him win the temptation battle? Have you drawn near to God lately? Is there a need to repent?

Reread James 4:7-10 and meditate on each area below. Write down any action steps you sense the Spirit leads you to take.

1. What do I need to give to God?

2. What do I need to get tough with Satan?

3. What do I need to get close to God?

4. What do I need to get right with others?

MEMORY VERSE: JAMES 4:10 (NASB)

Humble yourselves before the Lord and He will exalt you.

SESSION 3:
WHY WE WOUND OTHERS WITH WORDS

VIDEO NOTES:

> **LIE 2:** "IF OTHER PEOPLE WOULD SHAPE UP, MY LIFE WOULD WORK OUT."

[11]Brothers, do not slander one another. Anyone who speaks against his brother or judges him speaks against the law and judges it. When you judge the law, you are not keeping it, but sitting in judgment on it. [12]There is only one Lawgiver and Judge, the one who is able to save and destroy. But you – who are you to judge your neighbor? **JAMES 4: 11-12** (NIV)

We are commanded to stop "tearing one another down" by our "slanderous" speech.

-l- **WHAT IS "SLANDEROUS" SPEECH?**

-l- **HOW IS SLANDEROUS SPEECH COMMONLY PRACTICED?**

-l- **WHY DO EVEN SINCERE CHRISTIANS GET CAUGHT IN THE "WEB" OF SPEAKING AGAINST OTHERS?**

DISCUSSION QUESTIONS:

1. Have two or three people in the group briefly describe how some-one's words deeply wounded them.

2. What new insight have you gained about slander from Chip's teaching?

3. What is the significance of "brother" being mentioned so many times in James 4:11-12?

4. Chip listed three different degrees of slander that Christians practice:

-l- **1st degree** – Happens unintentionally in normal conversation

-l- **2nd degree** – Happens with "well meaning" prayer requests

-l- **3rd degree** – Happens under the guise of getting counsel on a difficult situation

Of the three, which one do you struggle with the most?

5. How did Chip's story at the end about the kids letting pink bubbles trickle into the river affect you?

ACTION STEPS:

FEW THINGS HAVE THE POWER TO RUIN RELATIONSHIPS LIKE CRITICAL, DEFAMING, AND SLANDEROUS WORDS

SLANDER HAPPENS ANYTIME THE RESULT OF OUR COMMUNICATION ABOUT SOMEONE (TRUTHFULLY OR NOT) BRINGS THEM LOW IN THE EYES OF ANOTHER

"Tale-bearing emits a threefold poison; for it injures the teller, the hearer and the person concerning whom the tale is told."

CHARLES SPURGEON

[1] Oswald Chambers, *My Utmost for His Highest : Selections for the Year* (Grand Rapids, MI: Discovery House Publishers, 1993, c1935), December 7.

Slander seeps into our conversation like water through a sieve. To have any hope of success, we must first understand why we seek to bring others low. Chip listed two reasons for why sincere believers get trapped in the web of speaking against each other:

Reason #1 – We believe the lie that if other people just shape up, things would go better for me.

Reason #2 – We have a perverse appetite for information.

Chances are you are presently in unhealthy conversations because of one of those two reasons. Take a few moments to think about your conversations in the past couple of weeks. Then take these courageous steps:

1. Have the courage to admit when you've sinned.

2. Have the courage to seek repentance from anyone if you have slandered their name.

3. Have the courage to refuse from entering into those conversations again.

AT HOME:

Fill in the blank: They will know we are Christians by our _____ .

How would the world fill in the same space? With "church splits"? "Backbiting"? "Gossip"?

Though the early church faced incredible persecution from outside its walls, the greatest battles were fought inside. Slander, criticism, and deadly rumors threatened to tear the fledgling organization to pieces. That's why we find so many "one another" passages throughout the New Testament. The authors of Scripture knew the constructive or destructive power of words.

In the chart on the next page, write down the attitude or action we are to have towards brothers and sisters within the church.

MEMORY VERSES: MATTHEW 12:36-37 (NIV)

"But I tell you that men will have to give account on the day of judgment for every careless word they have spoken. For by your words you will be acquitted, and by your words you will be condemned."

VERSE	ACTION OR ATTITUDE
John 13:33-34	
Romans 12:10	
Galatians 6:2	
Ephesians 4:25	
Hebrews 3:13	
Hebrews 10:24-25	

SESSION 4:
HOW TO STOP PLAYING GOD

VIDEO NOTES:

Why is "tearing others down" by our speech and judgmental attitudes one of the _____ **mentioned in Scripture?**

-|- **REASON #1 =** Because it demonstrates total disregard and contempt for God's highest command – to love one another. (Leviticus 19:18, James 2:8)

Anyone who speaks against his brother or judges him speaks against the law and judges it. When you judge the law, you are not keeping it, but sitting in judgment on it. **JAMES 4:11b** (NIV)

-|- **REASON #2 =** Because it reveals that we are in fact "playing God."

There is only one Lawgiver and Judge, the one who is able to save and destroy. But you – who are you to judge your neighbor? **JAMES 4:12** (NIV)

VIDEO NOTES:

How can we break the habit of "playing God"?

-|- **STEP #1** – Develop _____ about speaking against others.

> "Do not judge, or you too will be judged. For in the same way you judge others, you will be judged, and with the measure you use, it will be measured to you." **MATTHEW 7:1-2** (NIV)

> "But I tell you that men will have to give account on the day of judgment for every careless word they have spoken. For by your words you will be acquitted, and by your words you will be condemned." **MATTHEW 12:36-37** (NIV)

-|- **STEP #2** – Ponder the _____ of your speech.

> "A new command I give you: Love one another. As I have loved you, so you must love one another. By this all men will know that you are my disciples, if you love one another." **JOHN 13:34-35** (NIV)

-|- **STEP #3** – Refuse to buy _____!

> So when you, a mere man, pass judgment on them and yet do the same things, do you think you will escape God's judgment? **ROMANS 2:3** (NIV)

-|- **STEP #4** – Refuse to let others _____.

-|- **STEP #5** – _____ less!

> When words are many, sin is not absent, but he who holds his tongue is wise. **PROVERBS 10:19** (NIV)

> Don't criticize and speak evil about each other, dear brothers. If you do, you will be fighting against God's law of loving one another, declaring it is wrong. But your job is not to decide whether this law is right or wrong, but to obey it. Only He who made the law can rightly judge among us. He alone decides to save us or destroy. So what right do you have to judge or criticize others? **JAMES 4:11-12** (TLB)

DISCUSSION QUESTIONS:

1. Share in the group a story about how you apologized to someone and you thought it would go poorly, but God restored your relationship.

2. What did you find most helpful about Chip's teaching in this session?

3. Why, from God's perspective, is it so important that we speak about one another and relate in a loving manner? What's at stake?

4. Where do you find yourself most prone to "speak against" someone or become judgmental?

5. What are some practical and loving ways to inhibit others from continuing to gossip once they start?

SESSION 4:
KEYS

**TEARING SOME-
ONE DOWN WITH
WORDS IS ONE
OF THE MOST
SERIOUS SINS
IN THE BIBLE**

**WE NEED TO
FIGHT AGAINST
THE TEMPTATION
TO BOTH GOSSIP
AND LISTEN TO
GOSSIP**

*"A real Christian is the one
who can give his pet
parrot to the town gossip."*

BILLY GRAHAM

ACTION STEPS:

How often do we intentionally or unintentionally wound others with our words? At some point in time, we've all received the daggers from friends and relatives. Our character was questioned. We were double crossed. We were judged unfairly. But the real question to answer is who have we wounded?

Spend some time praying about this and determine to do whatever is necessary to bring healing.

AT HOME:

Write these steps down on an index card and find a time to meditate on them every day this week (i.e. drive time, while the kids are in school, etc.). As you think about the five steps to break the habit of "playing God," which one do you need to work on the most and why?

-|- **STEP #1** – Develop convictions about speaking against others.

-|- **STEP #2** – Ponder the consequences of your speech.

-|- **STEP #3** – Refuse to buy the lie!

-|- **STEP #4** – Refuse to let others gossip.

-|- **STEP #5** – Talk less!

MEMORY VERSES: JAMES 4:11-12 (TLB)

Don't criticize and speak evil about each other, dear brothers. If you do, you will be fighting against God's law of loving one another, declaring it is wrong. But your job is not to decide whether this law is right or wrong, but to obey it. Only he who made the law can rightly judge among us. He alone decides to save us or destroy. So what right do you have to judge or criticize others?

SESSION 5:
HOW OUR JOBS CAN DESTROY OUR RELATIONSHIPS

VIDEO NOTES:

INTRODUCTION: *Henry's "good job" was a bad deal!*

Why do we make bad job decisions?

-|- **EXHIBIT A** = James 4:13

Come now, you who say, "Today or tomorrow, we shall go to such and such a city, and spend a year there and engage in business and make a profit."
JAMES 4:13 (NASB)

The Business Plan Included:

-|- He chooses his _____.

-|- He selects his _____.

-|- He limits his _____.

-|- He defines his _____.

-|- He projects his _____.

VIDEO NOTES:

-I- **THE PROBLEM** = The Business Plan

The Business Plan Excluded _____.

Commit to the LORD, whatever you do, and your plans will succeed.
PROVERBS 16:3 (NIV)

In his heart a man plans his course, but the LORD determines his steps. **PROVERBS 16:9** (NIV)

> **SUMMARY: BAD DECISIONS ABOUT WORK FLOW FROM FALSE ASSUMPTIONS**

Why, you do not even know what will happen tomorrow. What is your life? You are a mist that appears for a little while and then vanishes. **JAMES 4:14** (NIV)

1. **FALSE ASSUMPTION #1** =
   Life is _____.

2. **FALSE ASSUMPTION #2** =
   Life is _____.

DISCUSSION QUESTIONS:

1. How do you personally include God in your decision making processes?

2. How did the story about Henry affect you? Was it challenging?

3. Have you ever made a decision that appeared "upwardly mobile" but in the end hurt your relationships? What did you learn from that experience?

4. Chip discussed two assumptions that people tend to make. Which one do you find yourself making and why?

5. Chip told a positive story at the end about how a business friend fasted before major decisions. What are some best practices you have seen modeled by friends or relatives to include God in business decisions?

IT'S EASY TO LEAVE GOD OUT OF OUR BUSINESS DECISIONS

THE ONLY GUARANTEE WE HAVE IN THIS TEMPORAL LIFE IS CHANGE

"If you have so much business to attend to that you have no time to pray, depend upon it, you have more business on hand than God ever intended you should have."

D.L. MOODY

ACTION STEPS:

Chip asserted that many of our decisions are based upon two key assumptions: "Life is predictable" and "Life is long." How would you live life if you reversed those assumptions?

-I- **LIFE IS UNPREDICTABLE**

-I- **LIFE IS SHORT**

What would you do? How would you live? What would you change about how you make decisions? This week, set up some time with a trusted friend at a coffee shop or a secluded place and share your thoughts. Make a change this week.

AT HOME:

Some have labeled James as the Proverbs of the New Testament. In these verses, we can see some real parallels with this Old Testament counterpart. Below are some verses from Proverbs. Look them up and write down a principle you can apply to any business or work situation (remember – moms and stay-at-home dads have the toughest job on earth!).

-|- **PROVERBS 4:5-6 –**

-|- **PROVERBS 3:9-10 –**

-|- **PROVERBS 11:24-25, 28 –**

-|- **PROVERBS 13:7, 22 –**

-|- **PROVERBS 21:5 –**

-|- **PROVERBS 22:1 –**

MEMORY VERSE: COLOSSIANS 3:23-24 (NASB)

Whatever you do, do your work heartily, as for the Lord rather than for men, knowing that from the Lord you will receive the reward of the inheritance. It is the Lord Christ whom you serve.

SESSION 6:
HOW TO PURSUE GOD-GIVEN DREAMS

VIDEO NOTES:

How Do We Make Wise Decisions About Work?

Instead, you ought to say, "If it is the Lord's will, we will live and do this or that." As it is, you boast and brag. All such boasting is evil. Anyone, then, who knows the good he ought to do and doesn't do it, sins.
JAMES 4: 15-17 (NIV)

1. Make _____ the foundation for all decision

   making. **v15**

2. Recognize the _____ of planning apart from God. **v16**

3. Don't buy the _____ .

> _____ _____ **WORK**
> **OPPORTUNITIES ARE AUTOMATICALLY**
> **THE WILL OF GOD**

DISCUSSION QUESTIONS:

1. What impacted you the most from this session?

2. Why is it difficult to believe that God has our best interests in mind?

3. When have you experienced God's help in a decision made at work?

4. Have you ever turned down something that was considered "upwardly mobile"? What helped you make that decision? How was it perceived by others?

5. What practical tip from Chip will you apply to your work decisions this week?

SESSION 6: KEYS

THOUGH IT'S DIFFICULT TO BELIEVE, GOD DOES HAVE OUR BEST INTERESTS AT HEART

WE TEND TO BELIEVE THE LIE THAT ANY UPWARDLY MOBILE OPPORTUNITY IS AUTOMATICALLY GOD'S WILL

"Belief that divine guidance is real rests upon two foundation-facts: first, the reality of God's plan for us; second, the ability of God to communicate with us. On both these facts the Bible has much to say."

J. I. PACKER

[1] Oswald Chambers, *My Utmost for His Highest : Selections for the Year* (Grand Rapids, MI: Discovery House Publishers, 1993, c1935), December 7.

ACTION STEPS:

Think about how we view God. We say He is good. But how often do we believe that with our head yet deny it with our hearts?

Take a few moments to meditate on this verse:

For the LORD God is a sun and shield; The LORD gives grace and glory; No good thing does He withhold from those who walk uprightly. **PSALM 84:11** (NASB)

What would change in your life if you actually believed God was "for you"?

AT HOME:

A noted Bible scholar, F.B. Meyer, once said, "When we want to know God's will, there are three things which always occur: the inward impulse, the Word of God, and the trend of circumstances.... Never act until these three things agree." Sometimes we make "discerning God's will" out to be harder than it is.

Chip listed four easy steps to help in knowing God's will on a particular decision:

1. Ask yourself, "Am I willing? Do I have an open heart?"

2. Pray

3. Look for a promise in God's Word

4. Seek wise counsel **(Proverbs 13:20)**

What decisions are you facing this week? Which steps do you need to put into practice? Take a moment to write these four steps on a note card and keep them with you throughout your work week.

MEMORY VERSES: JAMES 4:13-14 (NASB)

Come now, you who say, "Today or tomorrow we will go to such and such a city, and spend a year there and engage in business and make a profit." Yet you do not know what your life will be like tomorrow. You are just a vapor that appears for a little while and then vanishes away.

SESSION 7:
WHY BETTER THINGS DON'T ALWAYS MAKE THINGS BETTER

VIDEO NOTES:

> ## LIE 4: "MY SIGNIFICANCE AND VALUE ARE MEASURED BY THE QUALITY AND QUANTITY OF THE THINGS I POSSESS."

"If I had more money, I would be happier."
True or false? (circle one)

- -I- **EXHIBIT A =** Yesterday's Headlines
- -I- **EXHIBIT B =** Today's Relationships

The Lie

> MY _____ AND _____ IS MEAS-
> URED BY THE QUALITY AND QUANTITY OF
> THE THINGS I _____ . _____
> PROVIDE SECURITY AND POWER, SO I CAN
> BE SAFE, PERSONALLY SATISFIED, AND
> RULE MY WORLD.

Now listen, you rich people, weep and wail because of the misery that is coming upon you. Your wealth has rotted, and moths have eaten your clothes. Your gold and silver are corroded. Their corrosion will testify against you and eat your flesh like fire. You have hoarded wealth in the last days. Look! The wages you failed to pay the workmen who mowed your fields are crying out against you. The cries of the harvesters have reached the ears of the Lord Almighty. You have lived on earth in luxury and self-indulgence. You have fattened yourselves in the day of slaughter. You have condemned and murdered innocent men, who were not opposing you. **JAMES 5:1-6** (NASB)

Overview of the Passage:

- -I- Intended Audience
- -I- Historical Background
- -I- Structure of the Passage

VIDEO NOTES:

The Truth

> GOD _____ OPPOSED TO WEALTH. MANY OF THE GREATEST BELIEVERS IN THE BIBLE WERE WEALTHY; BUT GOD _____ OPPOSED TO THE MISUSE AND ABUSE OF WEALTH.

> **WARNING!** THE MISUSE OF WEALTH BRINGS GOD'S _____.

Now listen, you rich people, weep and wail because of the misery that is coming upon you." v1

> THE WRONG USES OF WEALTH – 4 **WARNINGS!**

1. **DON'T** _____!

Your wealth has rotted, and moths have eaten your clothes. Your gold and silver are corroded. Their corrosion will testify against you and eat your flesh like fire. You have hoarded wealth in the last days. v2-3

2. **DON'T** _____!

Look! The wages you failed to pay the workmen who mowed your fields are crying out against you. The cries of the harvesters have reached the ears of the Lord Almighty. v4

3. **DON'T** _____!

You have lived on earth in luxury and self-indulgence. You have fattened yourselves in the day of slaughter. v5

4. **DON'T** _____!

You have condemned and murdered innocent men, who were not opposing you. v6

DISCUSSION QUESTIONS:

1. What part of what Chip shared impacted you the most?

2. Why is money such a "hot button" in our relationships? What does money reveal about our inner attitudes and values?

3. How is "The Lie" sold to us daily? What are some general evidences that most of us buy much of "The Lie"?

4. How have you experienced the abuses of wealth as described by James 5:1-6?

5. What measures can we implement to keep us from buying things just because we can afford it?

SESSION 7: KEYS

WE MAY NOT BELIEVE IT INTELLECTUALLY, BUT EMOTIONALLY WE BELIEVE THE LIE THAT MORE MONEY OR MORE POSSESSIONS MAKES US MORE SATISFIED

OUR CHRISTIAN TESTIMONY IS AFFECTED POSITIVELY OR NEGATIVELY BY HOW WE HANDLE OUR MONEY

"Too many people spend money they haven't earned to buy things they don't want, to impress people they don't like."

WILL ROGERS

ACTION STEPS:

Few things reveal the state of our hearts like the state of our checkbooks. Jesus didn't mince words when He said, "You cannot serve both God and wealth." Look at Chip's four admonitions below. Beside each one, write down how you are doing on a scale of one to ten (1 being not good at all and 10 being really good).

1. Don't hoard it!

2. Don't steal it!

3. Don't waste it!

4. Don't abuse it!

Which one do you struggle with the most? Why is that? What is a practical step you can do this week to change your habits in one of these areas?

AT HOME:

One may think after a study like this that God opposes the rich. However, God blesses people with wealth and therefore has principles for them to follow. Take Chip's Bible Study challenge on the topic of wealth. Read 1 Timothy 6:17-19 (NASB).

> *Instruct those who are rich in this present world not to be conceited or to fix their hope on the uncertainty of riches, but on God, who richly supplies us with all things to enjoy. Instruct them to do good, to be rich in good works, to be generous and ready to share, storing up for themselves the treasure of a good foundation for the future, so that they may take hold of that which is life indeed.*

Take a few moments and write down at least five positive principles of how to use the wealth with which God has blessed you.

MEMORY VERSE: LUKE 16:13 (NASB)

No servant can serve two masters. Either he will hate the one and love the other, or he will be devoted to the one and despise the other. You cannot serve both God and Money.

SESSION 8:
USING WEALTH WISELY

VIDEO NOTES:

THE RIGHT USES OF WEALTH –
4 COMMANDS!

1. _____ it faithfully!

   The wise man saves for the future, but the foolish man spends whatever he gets. **PROVERBS 21:20** (TLB)

2. _____ it honestly!

   Work brings profit; talk brings poverty! **PROVERBS 14:23** (TLB)

   Let him who steals steal no longer; but rather let him labor, performing with his own hands what is good, in order that he may have something to share with him who has need. **EPHESIANS 4:28** (NASB)

3. _____ it wisely!

   Command those who are rich in this present world not to be arrogant nor to put their hope in wealth, which is so uncertain, but to put their hope in God, who richly provides us with everything for our enjoyment. Command them to do good, to be rich in good deeds, and to be generous and willing to share. **1 TIMOTHY 6:17-18** (NIV)

4. _____ it generously!

   One man gives freely, yet gains even more; another withholds unduly, but comes to poverty. A generous man will prosper; he who refreshes others will himself be refreshed. **PROVERBS 11:24-25** (NIV)

   It is more blessed to give than to receive. **ACTS 20:35** (NIV)

DISCUSSION QUESTIONS:

1. Take a few moments and share how this message impacted your life.

2. How can you live a lifestyle where you are in a healthy tension between radically sacrificing and radically enjoying the money God entrusts to you?

3. How does putting our financial house in order help our relational world?

4. Have you ever met someone who models a "lifestyle of generosity"? What habits did you admire the most?

5. If you could change one or two things about your financial picture right now, what would they be?

BIBLICAL SAVINGS ARE ABOUT STEWARDSHIP, NOT SECURITY

JESUS HAD MORE TO SAY ABOUT MONEY THAN ABOUT HEAVEN AND HELL COMBINED

"When I have any money, I get rid of it as quickly as possible, lest it find a way into my heart."

JOHN WESLEY

[1] Oswald Chambers, *My Utmost for His Highest : Selections for the Year* (Grand Rapids, MI: Discovery House Publishers, 1993, c1935), December 7.

ACTION STEPS:

Chip's summary statement was, "Until you get your financial house in order, your relational world will be in chaos." Set aside some time this week and ask yourself four questions about your money:

1. Am I saving it faithfully?

2. Am I earning it honestly?

3. Am I spending it wisely?

4. Am I giving it generously?

Remember, 100% of your money belongs to God, not just 10%. Implement the habits you need to keep those answers positive and then find an accountability partner to help you move from chaos to order.

AT HOME:

Though the Bible won't help you discern what stocks to buy, it is abundantly clear about how to manage your finances. Let's walk through the book of Proverbs again. Look up these verses and write down the financial principle being explained. Then ask yourself – "Am I living this out? If not, why not? What can I do this week to implement this principle?"

VERSE	PRINCIPLE
Proverbs 6:6-11	
Proverbs 13:11	
Proverbs 19:17	
Proverbs 23:4-5	
Proverbs 30:8-9	

MEMORY VERSE: LUKE 6:38 (NASB)

Give, and it will be given to you. They will pour into your lap a good measure—pressed down, shaken together, and running over. For by your standard of measure it will be measured to you in return.

SESSION 9:
WHY A CHANGE IN SCENERY RARELY IMPROVES THE VIEW

VIDEO NOTES:

LIE 5: "THE GRASS IS GREENER ON THE OTHER SIDE OF THE FENCE."

The Lie

> ### IF I COULD ONLY CHANGE _____, THEN EVERYTHING WOULD BE
> _____.

Under _____ we all tend to play the "if only..." game.

THE FALSE PREMISE: God wants me to be _____.

-|- **Major Premise =** God wants me to be happy

-|- **Minor Premise =** My situation, job, marriage, school, relationships are so painful/stressful that...

-|- **Conclusion =** This situation or relationship can't be God's will for my life.

The Truth

> ### RUNNING FROM ADVERSITY AND CONFLICT IN RELATIONSHIPS DOES NOT SOLVE PROBLEMS, BUT COMPOUNDS THEM.
> _____ **AND** _____
> ### ARE THE KEYS TO RELATIONAL TRANSFORMATION.

VIDEO NOTES:

Be patient, then, brothers, until the Lord's coming. See how the farmer waits for the land to yield its valuable crop and how patient he is for the autumn and spring rains.

You too, be patient and stand firm, because the Lord's coming is near.

Don't grumble against each other, brothers, or you will be judged. The Judge is standing at the door!

Brothers, as an example of patience in the face of suffering, take the prophets who spoke in the name of the Lord.

As you know, we consider blessed those who have persevered. You have heard of Job's perseverance and have seen what the Lord finally brought about. The Lord is full of compassion and mercy.

Above all, my brothers, do not swear—not by heaven or by earth or by anything else. Let your "Yes" be yes, and your "No," no, or you will be condemned.

JAMES 5: 7-12 (NIV)

LESSON FROM THE FARMER: We are commanded to be patient even when circumstances are beyond our control. v7-9

LESSONS FROM THE PROPHETS: We are commanded to be patient even when our circumstances are unfair and unjust. v7-9

DISCUSSION QUESTIONS:

1. Take a few minutes to play the "If Only" game. If only I could change (fill in the blank), then everything would be wonderful.

2. Just as Joseph went through a difficult and unfair situation, what hard times has God brought you through or is bringing you through?

3. Have you ever run from adversity only to discover that it did not solve the problems? Why is merely a "change of scenery" unable to change our hearts?

4. How can we develop a "long fuse" for trying and difficult situations?

5. What did the "farmer" and "prophet" teach us about perseverance?

SESSION 9:
KEYS

WHEN THERE IS PRESSURE IN OUR LIFE WE FALL UNDER THE TEMPTATION OF PLAYING THE "IF/ONLY" GAME

RUNNING FROM ADVERSITY NEVER SOLVES OUR PROBLEMS, IT ONLY COMPOUNDS THEM

"God whispers to us in our pleasures, speaks in our conscience, but shouts in our pain: it is his megaphone to rouse a deaf world."

C.S. LEWIS

ACTION STEPS:

Regardless of our trials and tribulations, chances are, they pale in comparison to what Joseph endured. If anyone had a right to complain about "greener grass" it was Joseph. If you need further background to his trials, read Genesis 37-50. Then ask yourself, "Would I have responded in the same way?"

Read his response in Genesis 50:12-21.
Whether it's a bad job situation or difficult relationship, what is God asking you to endure until He delivers you for His good purpose?

AT HOME:

Any general will tell you – the key to victory is securing the high ground. Unfortunately, in the daily battles we face, the most coveted ground is our minds. If we want to ward off the Enemy's darts, we must shield our minds with the Word. Chip talked about two key words in our study:

- **Patience** – "enduring someone who is incompatible for a long time"

- **Perseverance** – "tolerating a circumstance or a difficulty for a long time"

One definition has to do with a hard person and the other a hard place. You are probably under pressure in one of those areas. And the Enemy will do all he can to make you believe it's better for you to take flight than fight. Put a few arrows in your quiver by meditating on these passages. Ask yourself the question – what does God want to produce in me through patience and perseverance?

- Romans 5:1-5
- Hebrews 6:11-12
- Hebrews 10:36-39
- James 1:2-4
- 1 Peter 2:19-20
- 2 Peter 1:5-11

MEMORY VERSE: JOHN 16:33 (NASB)

"These things I have spoken to you, so that in Me you may have peace. In the world you have tribulation, but take courage; I have overcome the world."

HOW PATIENCE AND PERSEVERANCE TRANSFORM RELATIONSHIPS

VIDEO NOTES:

As you know, we consider blessed those who have persevered. You have heard of Job's perseverance and have seen what the Lord finally brought about. The Lord is full of compassion and mercy. Above all, my brothers, do not swear—not by heaven or by earth or by anything else. Let your "Yes" be yes, and your "No," no, or you will be condemned.

JAMES 5:11-12 (NIV)

LESSON FROM JOB: We are commanded to persevere, even when we don't understand why God is allowing such adversity in our lives. v11

APPLICATION: We are commanded to demonstrate our patience and perseverance by keeping our vows and commitments. v12

DISCUSSION QUESTIONS:

1. If you are in a mixed group of men and women, you may want to separate into same gender groups. Then, as the Lord leads you, share any issue you might be facing where you are tempted to give up. If appropriate share a few of them in the group when you come back together.

2. What lesson did we learn from Job about perseverance?

3. Why do we assume God has left us in the midst of struggles? What gave the disciples such a different perspective?

4. Why is keeping our promises crucial when we live in an "exception clause" world?

5. Now that your group has finished this study, what is your next step towards becoming more like Christ?

SESSION 10:
KEYS

GOD DESIRES TO DELIVER US THROUGH OUR STRUGGLES, NOT OUT OF THEM SO THAT WE MIGHT DEVELOP INTO THE IMAGE OF CHRIST

WHEN WE CANNOT SEE GOD OR HIS HAND, TRUST HIS HEART HAS OUR BEST INTERESTS IN MIND

"There is no pit so deep that God's love is not deeper still."

CORRIE TEN BOOM

[1] Oswald Chambers, *My Utmost for His Highest : Selections for the Year* (Grand Rapids, MI: Discovery House Publishers, 1993, c1935), December 7.

ACTION STEPS:

Our culture bombards us with lies on a daily basis. To ward off fiery darts of insecurities and anxieties, Chip carried around Psalm 34 on an index card. Take a few moments to write down part of this psalm on one side of a card. On the backside, write down in your own words, God's encouragement or promise for you. When anxious thoughts weigh down on you, push against the resistance with His truth.

PSALM 34:4-10; 17-18

AT HOME:

As you look back over the past ten weeks, how have you changed? What will you take away from this study? It's tempting to leave all of these timeless truths safely tucked away in the pages of this study guide. Below you will find the five lies that ruin relationships. Beside each one, write down the truth to combat the lie and a specific way you are going to change in that area

1. **LIE 1: "SENSUAL PLEASURE WILL SATISFY MY INNER LONGINGS FOR HAPPINESS."**

2. **LIE 2: "IF OTHER PEOPLE WOULD SHAPE UP, MY LIFE WOULD WORK OUT."**

3. **LIE 3: "UPWARDLY MOBILE WORK OPPORTUNITIES ARE AUTOMATICALLY THE WILL OF GOD."**

4. **LIE 4: "MY SIGNIFICANCE AND VALUE ARE MEASURED BY THE QUALITY AND QUANTITY OF THE THINGS I POSSESS."**

5. **LIE 5: "THE GRASS IS GREENER ON THE OTHER SIDE OF THE FENCE."**

MEMORY VERSE: **JAMES 5:12** (NASB)

But above all, my brethren, do not swear, either by heaven or by earth or with any other oath; but your yes is to be yes, and your no, no, so that you may not fall under judgment.

FIVE LIES THAT RUIN RELATIONSHIPS

THE TOOLS FOR THIS SERIES

GETTING STARTED - 3 EASY STEPS

Several basic ingredients are essential to any successful group study. Before you plan the first meeting, you should work through these fundamentals.

1. First, pray! Only God can change the hearts of men, and prayer is your most powerful tool.

2. Next, organize. Consider asking one or two others to share the leadership load by helping you plan, bring refreshments, distribute materials, etc.

3. Prepare to lead the sessions. Preview the video and the Study Guide each week before the group arrives.

THINGS TO REMEMBER WHILE LEADING THIS SERIES

TRIED AND TRUE TIPS FOR THE SUCCESSFUL VIDEO SERIES LEADER

BE YOURSELF: The others in your group will appreciate and follow your example of openness and honesty as you lead - so set a good example! The best way to encourage those in your group is with your sincere desire to live out these principles in your own life. When they sense that you are "real" – that you are not "above" the issues that challenge them – they will be encouraged to press on.

BE PREPARED: Hopefully, the discussion questions will raise some interesting conversation in your group. However, you can also lose focus during discussion time as people present opinions that may detract from the focus of the lesson, or may not represent Biblical teaching. A good way to keep things on track is to point the conversation back to the materials.

ABOUT YOUR VIDEO TEACHER

Chip Ingram is your teacher for *Five Lies that Ruin Relationships*. Chip Ingram is the president and teaching pastor of *Living on the Edge*. Chip's successful radio program, which began in 1995, has expanded to more than 800 radio outlets nationwide. A graduate of Dallas Theological Seminary, Chip has a unique ability to communicate biblical truth in a way that brings about transformation in lives. He and his wife, Theresa, have four grown children.

HOW TO STRUCTURE YOUR GROUP TIME

Whether you are leading this series in Sunday school or a small group in a home, you'll find the materials are ideal for most group settings. The course is designed so that the video teaching and the discussion questions will fit into hour segments. Of course, you can take extra time for discussion or to review the previous week's material if time permits.

Below is the suggested way to use these materials:

IN CLASS

1. **VIDEO CLASS NOTES:** Each video session has a corresponding section in the Study Guide for participants to follow along as Chip teaches. A fill-in-the-blank outline highlights the main points of the video, and there is room for additional notes and insights as well. The "answers" to the notes can be found in the Leader's Guide for each session.

2. **DISCUSSION QUESTIONS:** The Study Guide also contains discussion questions for each of the video sessions. They are designed to help your participants personalize the content of each lesson. You can move to these questions immediately after the conclusion of the video.

   The main goal of these questions is to help you stir up discussion in your group. Encourage your group to answer with more than short "yes" and "no" answers. Use the questions to draw people into discussing their hearts, their struggles, and how the teaching could be applied to their personal situations.

3. **ACTION STEPS:** The Study Guide then moves into specific action steps that are designed to help create specific ways to apply the material. Your group will benefit tremendously by sharing ideas and discussing the recommended action steps together. Be sure to be honest and transparent during this time. Make it clear that you are a fellow-learner, not an untouchable "expert" on the Bible and relationships. Make your group a safe environment for sharing personal struggles. Together, your group can minister to each other, helping to apply God's Word to everyday situations.

AFTER CLASS

4. **AT HOME:** These personal studies are intended to take the principles right off the page and into the lives of each student. This is where the series moves from contemplation to application. Encourage the people in your group to complete their assignments weekly.

SUGGESTED FORMAT

1. View the Video Lesson, filling in the notes in the Study Guide (25-30 minutes)

2. Discussion Questions (25 minutes)

3. Assignment for upcoming week (5 minutes)

4. Prayer requests, group prayer (10 minutes)

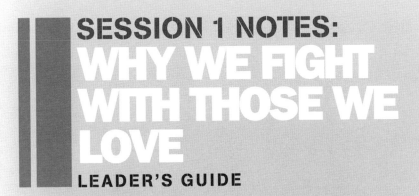

SESSION 1 NOTES:
WHY WE FIGHT WITH THOSE WE LOVE

LEADER'S GUIDE

VIDEO NOTES

ANSWER KEY:

The root cause of interpersonal conflicts is our consuming passion for <u>self–gratification</u>.

- -I- OUR PROBLEM = <u>Selfish Pride</u>

- -I- THE SYMPTOMS = <u>Conflict</u>

- -I- OUR STRATEGY =
  <u>1. We attempt to fulfill our desires apart from God.</u>
  <u>2. We try to use God to fulfill our selfish desire.</u>

- -I- THE RESULTS = <u>Frustration within, fights without</u>

GOD'S DIAGNOSIS: Our constant quarrels reveal . . .

1. <u>We've believed a lie.</u>

2. <u>We've betrayed a trust.</u>

3. <u>We've become an enemy.</u>

SESSION 2 NOTES:
DEFUSING CONFLICT... RESTORING RELATIONSHIPS

LEADER'S GUIDE

VIDEO NOTES

God's Prescription: <u>Humble yourselves</u> and God will heal your relationships. v 7-10

STEPS TO DEFUSE CONFLICT

1. <u>Give in to God - Surrender</u>

2. <u>Get tough with Satan - Fight</u>

3. <u>Get close to God - Return</u>

4. <u>Get right with others - Stop Sinning</u>

GOD'S PROMISE FOR THE HUMBLE v10

<u>Humble yourself and He will exalt you!</u>

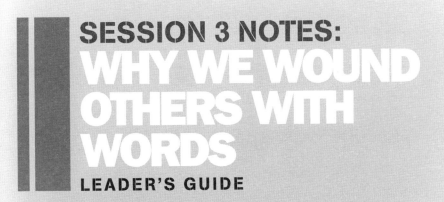

SESSION 3 NOTES:
WHY WE WOUND OTHERS WITH WORDS
LEADER'S GUIDE

VIDEO NOTES

ANSWER KEY:

-I- WHAT IS "SLANDEROUS" SPEECH?

Saying something untrue, motive is to tear them down. In conversation, when other leaves, he thinks less of the person slandered than when the conversation started.

-I- HOW IS SLANDEROUS SPEECH COMMONLY PRACTICED?

- *Normal conversation*
- *Prayer requests*
- *Seeking advice for a problem situation*

-I- WHY DO EVEN SINCERE CHRISTIANS GET CAUGHT IN THE "WEB" OF SPEAKING AGAINST OTHERS?

- *We believe the lie, "If ___ would just shape up, then my life would be better"*
- *"The problem isn't me, it's ____"*

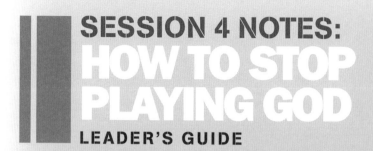

SESSION 4 NOTES:
HOW TO STOP
PLAYING GOD
LEADER'S GUIDE

VIDEO NOTES

ANSWER KEY:

Why is "tearing others down" by our speech and judgmental attitudes one of the <u>most serious sins</u> mentioned in Scripture?

How can we break the habit of "playing God"?

-|- **STEP #1** – Develop **<u>convictions</u>** about speaking against others.

-|- **STEP #2** – Ponder the **<u>consequences</u>** of your speech.

-|- **STEP #3** – Refuse to buy **<u>the lie</u>**!

-|- **STEP #4** – Refuse to let others **<u>gossip</u>**.

-|- **STEP #5** – **<u>Talk</u>** less!

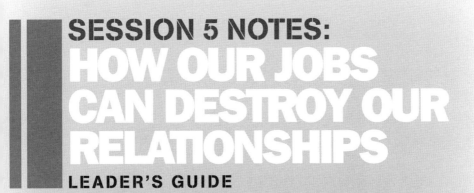

SESSION 5 NOTES:
HOW OUR JOBS CAN DESTROY OUR RELATIONSHIPS

LEADER'S GUIDE

VIDEO NOTES

ANSWER KEY:

The Business Plan Included:

-I- He chooses his **Selfish Pride**.

-I- He selects his **Location**.

-I- He limits his **Stay**.

-I- He defines his **Market**.

-I- He projects his **Profits**.

THE PROBLEM = The Business Plan Excluded God.

Summary = Bad Decisions about work flow from false assumptions.

1. FALSE ASSUMPTION #1 = Life is **predictable**.
2. FALSE ASSUMPTION #2 = Life is **long**.

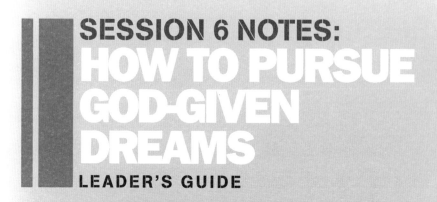

SESSION 6 NOTES:
HOW TO PURSUE GOD-GIVEN DREAMS
LEADER'S GUIDE

VIDEO NOTES

How Do We Make Wise Decisions About Work?

1. Make **God's will** the foundation for all decision making. **v15**

2. Recognize the **root cause** of planning apart from God. **v16**

3. Don't buy the **lie**.

THE LIE: **UPWARDLY MOBILE** WORK OPPORTUNITIES ARE AUTOMATICALLY THE WILL OF GOD.

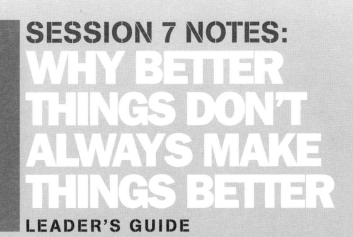

SESSION 7 NOTES:
WHY BETTER THINGS DON'T ALWAYS MAKE THINGS BETTER
LEADER'S GUIDE

VIDEO NOTES

ANSWER KEY:

THE LIE: MY **SIGNIFICANCE** AND **VALUE** IS MEASURED BY THE QUALITY AND QUANTITY OF THE THINGS I **POSSESS**. **POSSESSIONS** PROVIDE SECURITY AND POWER, SO I CAN BE SAFE, PERSONALLY SATISFIED, AND RULE MY WORLD.

THE TRUTH: GOD **IS NOT** OPPOSED TO WEALTH. MANY OF THE GREATEST BELIEVERS IN THE BIBLE WERE WEALTHY; BUT GOD **IS** OPPOSED TO THE MISUSE AND ABUSE OF WEALTH.

WARNING! THE MISUSE OF WEALTH BRINGS GOD'S **JUDGMENT**.

1. Don't **hoard it**!

2. Don't **steal it**!

3. Don't **waste it**!

4. Don't **abuse it**!

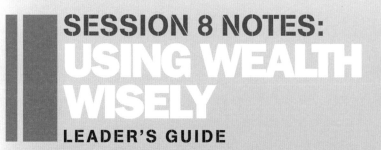

SESSION 8 NOTES:
USING WEALTH WISELY
LEADER'S GUIDE

VIDEO NOTES

ANSWER KEY:

THE RIGHT USES OF WEALTH – 4 COMMANDS!

1. **Save** it faithfully!
2. **Make** it honestly!
3. **Spend** it wisely!
4. **Give** it generously!

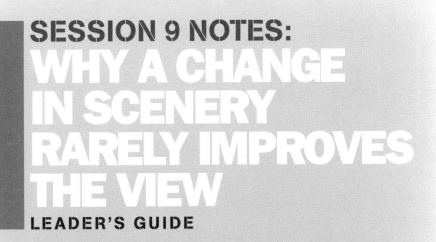

SESSION 9 NOTES:
WHY A CHANGE IN SCENERY RARELY IMPROVES THE VIEW
LEADER'S GUIDE

VIDEO NOTES

ANSWER KEY:

THE LIE: "THE GRASS IS GREENER ON THE OTHER SIDE OF THE FENCE" MENTALITY. IF I COULD ONLY CHANGE _____ THEN EVERYTHING WOULD BE **WONDERFUL**.

Under **pressure** we all tend to play the "if only..." game.

THE FALSE PREMISE: God wants me to be **happy**.

THE TRUTH: RUNNING FROM ADVERSITY AND CONFLICT IN RELATIONSHIPS DOES NOT SOLVE PROBLEMS, BUT COMPOUNDS THEM. **PATIENCE** AND **PERSEVERANCE** ARE THE KEYS TO RELATIONAL TRANSFORMATION.

SESSION 10 NOTES:
HOW PATIENCE AND PERSEVERANCE TRANSFORM RELATIONSHIPS

LEADER'S GUIDE

VIDEO NOTES *There are no fill-in-the-blanks in this session.*

what's next?

If your group would like to go deeper in their understanding of the Five Lies that Ruin Relationships, consider one of the following studies:

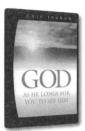

SURRENDER...
God: As He Longs for You to See Him
How would you describe God? Awesome? All Powerful? Creator? While we cannot know Him exhaustively, we can know Him truly. And God longs for you to see Him as He truly is. Join Chip in this fascinating series studying the seven attributes of God.

SEPARATE FROM THE WORLD...
Miracle of Life Change
Is life change really possible? If we're honest most of us would answer, "No." You've tried numerous programs that promise big changes, but in reality, deliver very little results. You long for transformation, but don't know where to begin. There's good news for you and there is hope. Life change is possible!

SOBER IN SELF-ASSESSMENT...
Your Divine Design
Do you know how God has uniquely wired you? Every believer was created to play a strategic role in the body of Christ with the gifts God has given them. But many of today's Christians face one difficult question—how do I discover my spiritual gifts and use them effectively in my church?

SUPERNATURALLY RESPONDING TO EVIL WITH GOOD...
Invisible War
Beneath our tangible landscape lurks an invisible spiritual realm where an unseen battle rages. It's real and it's dangerous. If you're prepared to remove the blinders and gaze into the unseen world, Chip is ready to take you there.

The Living on the Edge Community.

Over 40 Online Growth Resources + the r12 Online Experience...FREE!

It's jam-packed full of free audio & video resources from Chip Ingram and others to help make your faith real. You can watch, listen, download messages and share with your friends.

All New Community Features

- Video Messages
- Audio Messages
- MP3 Downloads
- Community Blog
- Chip's Corner
- Resource Sharing

Grow Deeper with the r12 Online Experience

A new guided discipleship pathway from Living on the Edge based on Romans chapter 1

All the Features You Remember & More

- Radio Offers
- Listen Online
- Radio Broadcasts
- Podcasts
- TV Broadcasts
- Message Notes

Join now to experience
the New Living on the Edge
Community & r12 online today

LivingontheEdge.org